C000186162

# Pub Singalong
## 23 classic songs for keyboard

© International Music Publications Ltd
First published in 1996 by International Music Publications Ltd
International Music Publications Ltd is a Faber Music company
Bloomsbury House 74–77 Great Russell Street London WC1B 3DA
Cover Image © Hulton-Deutsch Collection/CORBIS
Music arranged & processed by Barnes Music Engraving Ltd
Printed in England by Caligraving Ltd
All rights reserved

ISBN10: 0-571-53090-7
EAN13: 978-0-571-53090-8

# Ain't That A Grand And Glorious Feeling

*Words and Music by Milton Ager and Jack Yellen*

**Suggested Registration:** Honky Tonk Piano
**Rhythm:** Swing
**Tempo:** ♩ = 160

# Alexander's Ragtime Band

Words and Music by Irving Berlin

**Suggested Registration:** Clarinet
**Rhythm:** Dixieland
**Tempo:** ♩ = 160

Come on and hear,_____ come on and hear A - lex -

- an - der's rag - time band,_____ come on and hear,_____ come on and

hear, it's the best band in the land. They can play a bu - gle call like you

ne - ver heard be - fore, so na - tu - ral that you want to go to war,

that's just the best - est band what am,

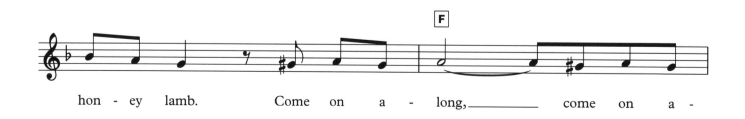

hon - ey lamb. Come on a - long,_____ come on a -

# Are You Lonesome Tonight?

*Words and Music by Roy Turk and Lou Handman*

**Suggested Registration:** Saxophone
**Rhythm:** Waltz
**Tempo:** ♩ = 92

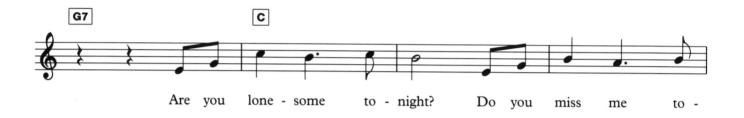

Are you lone - some to - night? Do you miss me to -

- night? Are you sor - ry we drift - ed a - part?_____

— Does your me - mo - ry stray to a bright sum - mer

day when I kissed you, and called you, 'Sweet - heart?'_____

Do the chairs in your par - lour seem emp - ty and

bare? Do you gaze at your door - step, and pic - ture me

there? Is your heart filled with pain? Shall I come back a -

- gain? Tell me dear, are you lone - some to - night?_____

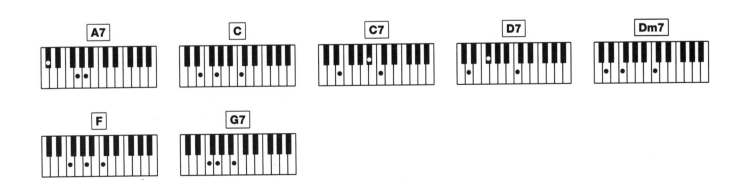

# Bye Bye Blackbird

Words by Mort Dixon / Music by Ray Henderson

**Suggested Registration:** Muted Trumpet
**Rhythm:** Swing
**Tempo:** ♩ = 152

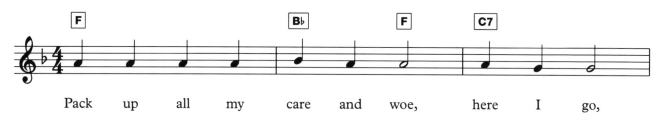

Pack up all my care and woe, here I go,

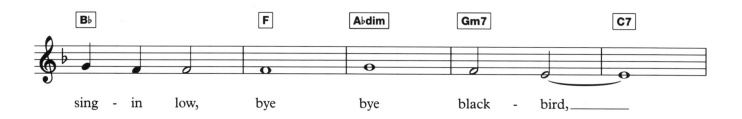

sing - in low, bye bye black - bird, _____

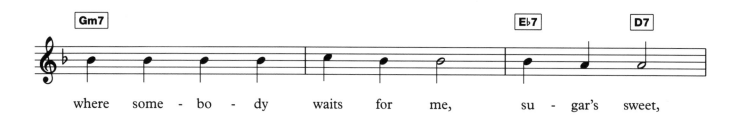

where some - bo - dy waits for me, su - gar's sweet,

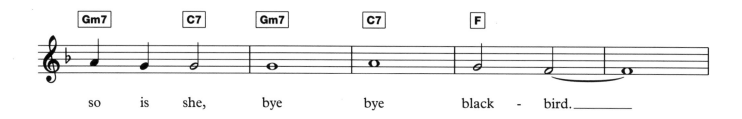

so is she, bye bye black - bird. _____

No one else can love or un - der - stand me,

Francis Day & Hunter Ltd, London WC2H 0EA and Redwood Music Ltd, London NW1 8BD

oh, what hard luck sto - ries they all hand me.

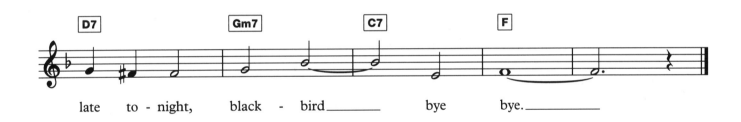

Make my bed and light the light, I'll ar - rive

late to - night, black - bird_____ bye bye._____

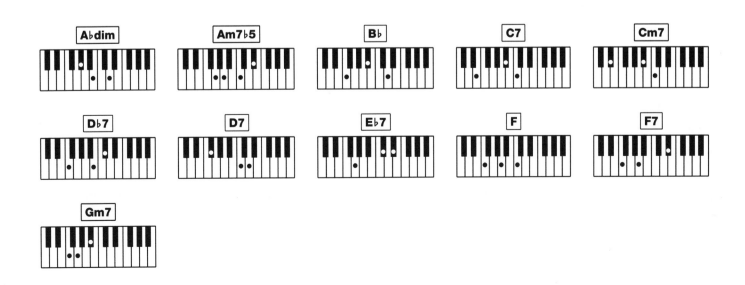

# Carolina In The Morning

Words By Gus Kahn / Music by Walter Donaldson

**Suggested Registration:** Clarinet
**Rhythm:** Swing
**Tempo:** ♩ = 144

No - thing could be fi - ner than to be in Ca - ro - li - na in the

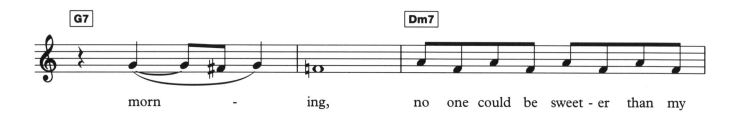

morn - ing, no one could be sweet - er than my

love - ly when I meet her in the morn - ing, where the morn - ing

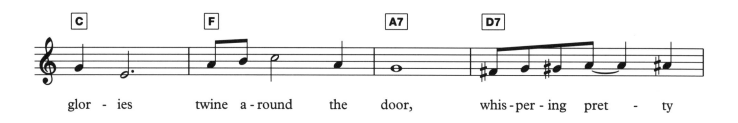

glor - ies twine a - round the door, whis - per - ing pret - ty

stor - ies I long to hear__ once more. Stroll - ing with my girl - ie, where the

dew is pearl - y, ear - ly in the morn - ing,

but - ter - flies all flut - ter up, and kiss each lit - tle but - ter - cup at dawn -

- ing. If I had A - lad - din's lamp for on - ly a day, ___

I'd make a wish, and here's what I'd say, ___ 'No - thing could be fi - ner than to

be in Ca - ro - li - na in the morn - ing.'

# Carolina Moon

Words and Music by Benny Davis and Joe Burke

**Suggested Registration:** Accordian *master*
**Rhythm:** Waltz
**Tempo:** ♩ = 104

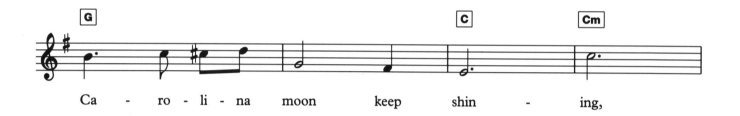

Ca - ro - li - na moon keep shin - ing,

shin - ing on the one who waits for me.

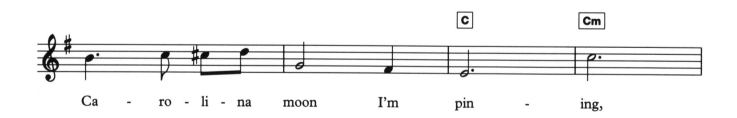

Ca - ro - li - na moon I'm pin - ing,

pin - ing for the place I long to be. How I'm

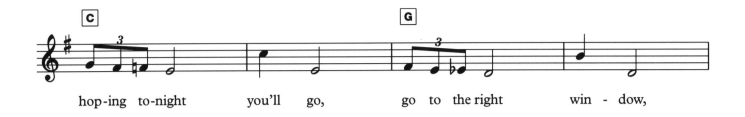

hop-ing to-night you'll go, go to the right win - dow,

scat - ter your light, say I'm al-right, please do._____

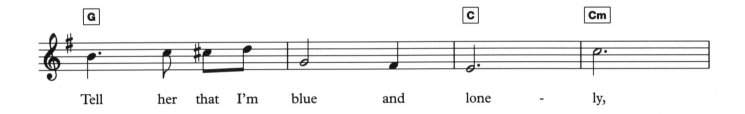

Tell her that I'm blue and lone - ly,

dream - y Ca - ro - li - na moon._____

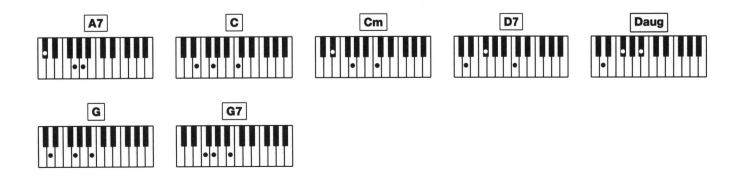

# Delilah

Words and Music by Les Reed and Barry Mason

**Suggested Registration:** Saxophone
**Rhythm:** Waltz
**Tempo:** ♩ = 156

I saw the light on the night that I passed by her

win - dow._____

I saw the flick - er - ing sha - dows of love on her

blind._____ She_____

was_____ my wo - man._____

As she de - ceived me I watched, and went out of my mind._____

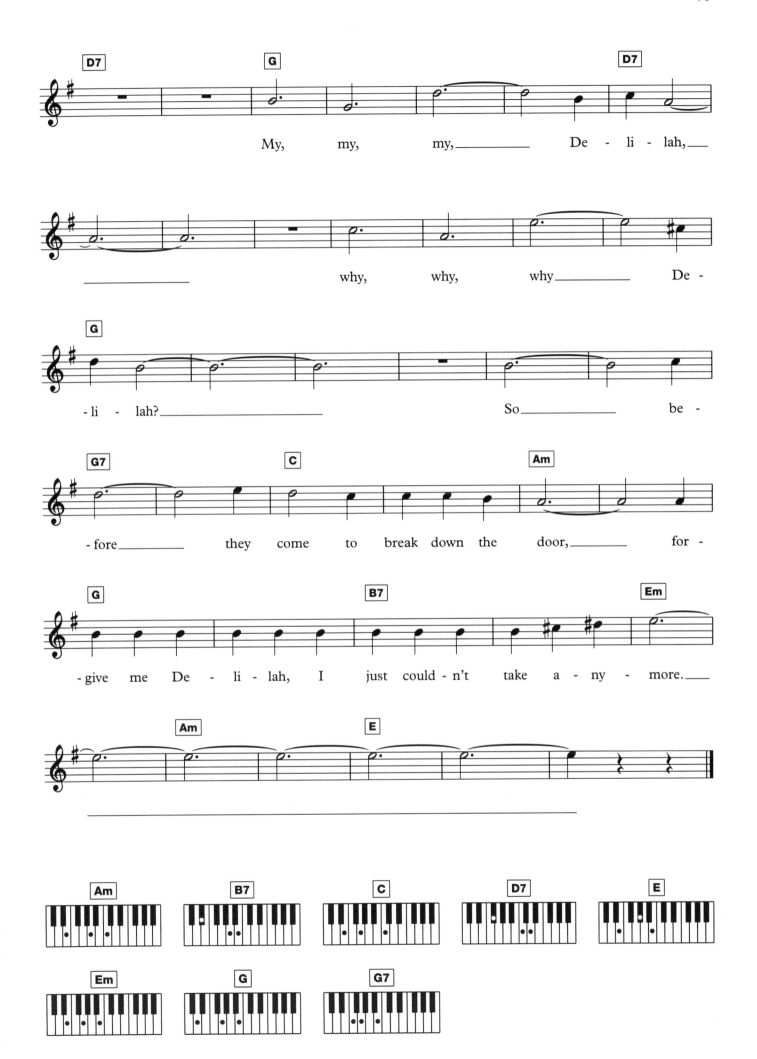

# Glorious Beer

Words by Steve Leggett / Music by Will Godwin

**Suggested Registration:** Accordian
**Rhythm:** Waltz
**Tempo:** ♩ = 160

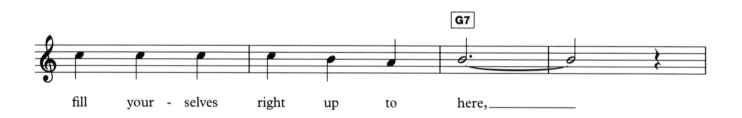

Beer,      beer,      glo - ri - ous beer,

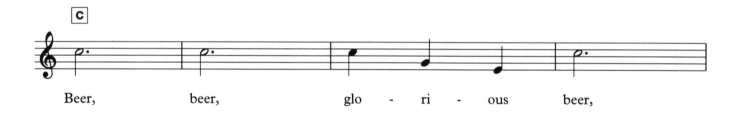

fill   your - selves   right   up   to   here,_____

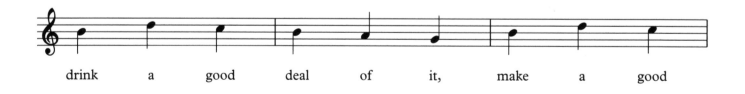

drink   a   good   deal   of   it,   make   a   good

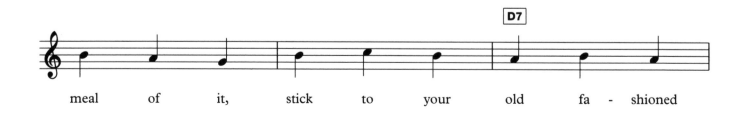

meal   of   it,   stick   to   your   old   fa - shioned

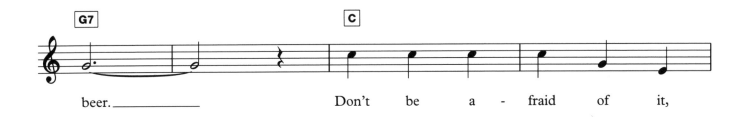

beer._____ Don't be a - fraid of it,

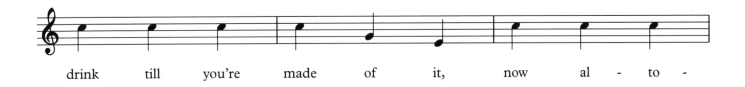

drink till you're made of it, now al - to -

- ge - ther, a cheer!_____ Up with the

sale of it, down with a pail of it,

glo - ri - ous, glo - ri - ous beer!_____

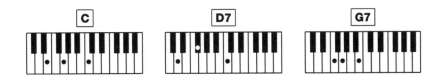

# I'm Looking Over A Four Leaf Clover

Words by Mort Dixon / Music by Harry Woods

**Suggested Registration:** Jazz Organ
**Rhythm:** Swing
**Tempo:** ♩ = 200

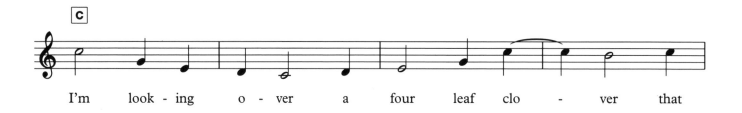

I'm look-ing o - ver a four leaf clo - ver that

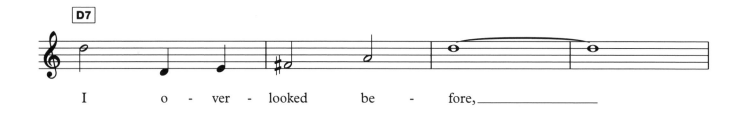

I o - ver - looked be - fore,_____

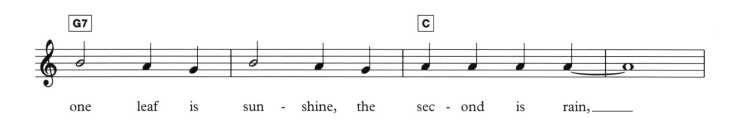

one leaf is sun - shine, the sec - ond is rain,_____

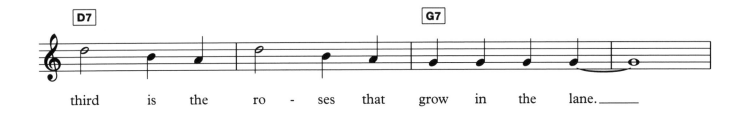

third    is    the    ro  -  ses    that    grow    in    the    lane._____

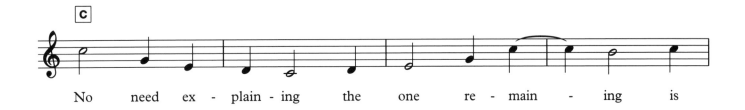

No    need    ex  -  plain  -  ing    the    one    re  -  main  -  ing    is

some  -  bo  -  dy    I    a  -  dore,_____

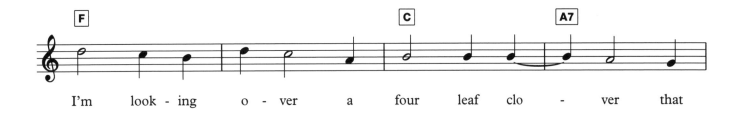

I'm    look  -  ing    o  -  ver    a    four    leaf    clo  -  ver    that

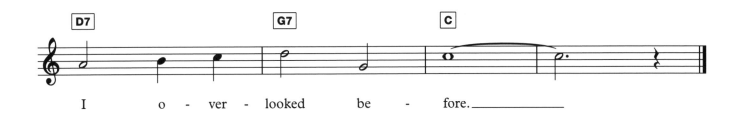

I    o  -  ver  -  looked    be  -  fore._____

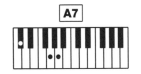
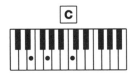

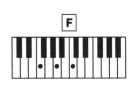
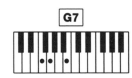

# Lily The Pink

Adapted and arranged by John Gorman, Mike McGear and Roger McGough

**Suggested Registration:** Honky Tonk Piano
**Rhythm:** Shuffle
**Tempo:** ♩. = 120

We'll drink a drink a drink to Li - ly the Pink, the Pink, the

Pink, the sav - iour of_____ the hu - man race,_____

__ for she in - vent - ed_____ me - di - ci - nal

com - pound,____ most ef - fi - ca - cious____ in ev - ery

case._____ Oh!_____ Oh!_____

Oh!_____ We'll_____

drink a drink a drink to Li - ly the Pink, the Pink, the

Pink, the sav - iour of_____ the hu - man race,_____

_ for she in - vent - ed_____ me - di - ci - nal com - pound,_

_ most ef - fi - ca - cious_____ in ev - ery case.

# Love Letters In The Sand

Words by Nick Kenny and Charles Kenny / Music by J Fred Coots

**Suggested Registration:** Clarinet
**Rhythm:** Swing
**Tempo:** ♩ = 144

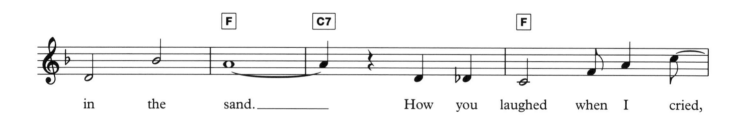

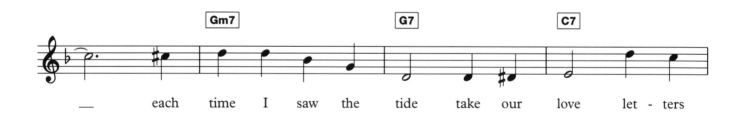

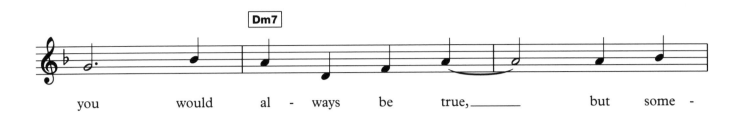

you    would    al - ways    be    true,_____    but    some -

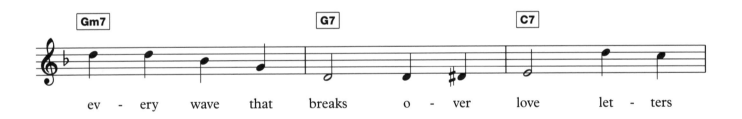

- how    that    vow    meant    no - thing    to    you.____

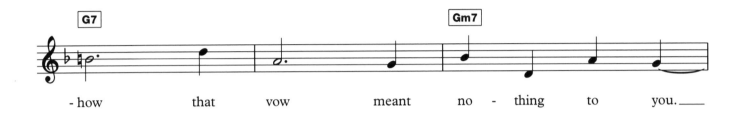

___    Now    my    poor    heart    just    aches____    with

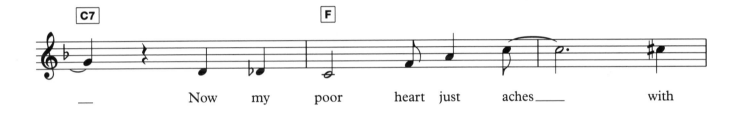

ev - ery    wave    that    breaks    o - ver    love    let - ters

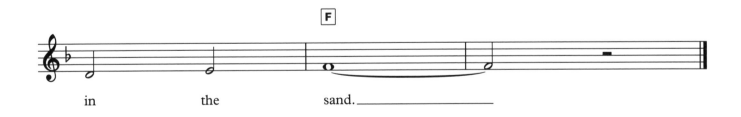

in    the    sand._____

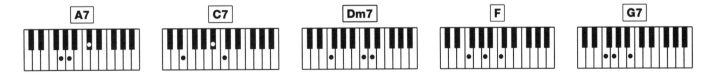

# Peg O' My Heart

Words by Alfred Bryan / Music by Fred Fisher

**Suggested Registration:** Vibraphone
**Rhythm:** Slow Swing
**Tempo:** ♩ = 92

Peg o' my heart,_____ I love you, don't let us part,\_\_\_\_\_

\_ I love you. I al - ways knew\_ it would be you,\_

since I heard your lilt - ing laugh - ter, it's your I - rish heart I'm af - ter.

Peg o' my heart,_____ your glan - ces make my heart say,\_\_\_\_\_

\_ 'How's chan - ces?' Come, be my own,\_ come make your home in my heart.

Ascherberg Hopwood & Crew Ltd, London W1Y 3FA and Redwood Music Ltd, London NW1 8BD

Peg o' my heart,_____ I love you, we'll ne - ver part,_____

__ I love you, dear lit - tle girl,__ sweet lit - tle girl,__

sweet - er than the rose of E - rin are your win - ning smiles en - dear - ing.

Peg o' my heart,_____ your glan - ces, with I - rish art_____ en - trance us.

Come, be my own,_ come make your home in my heart._____

# Red Roses For A Blue Lady

*Words and Music by Sid Tepper and Roy C Bennett*

**Suggested Registration:** Vibraphone
**Rhythm:** Swing
**Tempo:** ♩ = 160

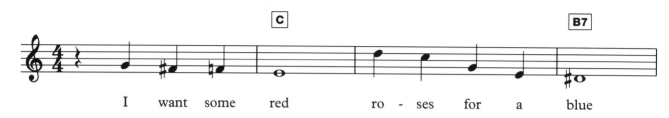

I want some red ro - ses for a blue

la - dy, Mis - ter Flor - ist take my or - der please,____

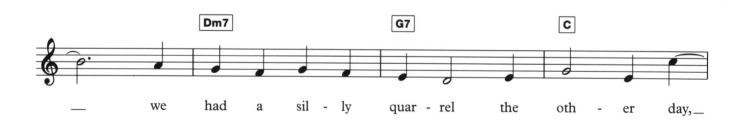

___ we had a sil - ly quar - rel the oth - er day, __

___ hope these pret - ty flow - ers chase her

blues a - way._____ Wrap up some red

ro - ses    for    a    blue    la - dy,    send    them    to    the

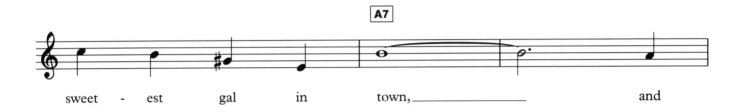

sweet - est    gal    in    town,_____    and

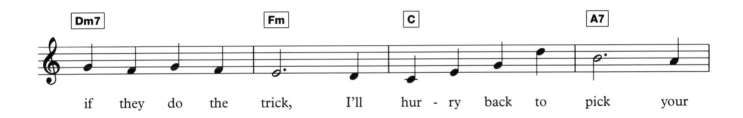

if    they    do    the    trick,    I'll    hur - ry    back    to    pick    your

best    white    or - chid    for    her    wed - ding    gown._____

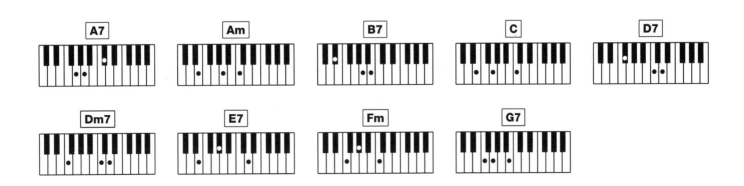

# SALLY

Words and Music by Will Haines, Harry Leon and Leo Towers

**Suggested Registration:** Strings
**Rhythm:** Waltz
**Tempo:** ♩ = 112

Sal - ly, Sal - ly don't ev - er wan - der a -

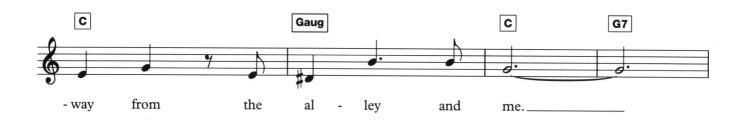

- way from the al - ley and me._____

Sal - ly, Sal - ly, mar - ry me

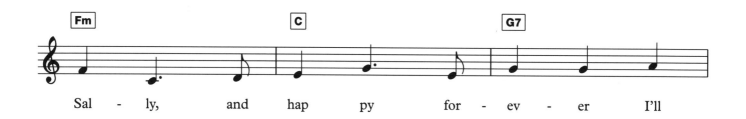

Sal - ly, and hap - py for - ev - er I'll

# Shine On Harvest Moon

Words by Jack Norworth / Music by Nora Bayes

**Suggested Registration:** Accordian
**Rhythm:** Shuffle
**Tempo:** ♩ = 100

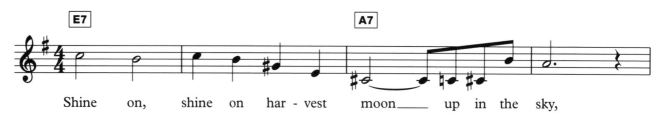

Shine on, shine on har-vest moon___ up in the sky,

I ain't had no lov-in' since Jan-u-a-ry, Feb-ru-a-ry,

June or Ju-ly.___ Snow time ain't no time to

stay___ out-doors and spoon, so shine on,

shine on har-vest moon, for me and my gal.___

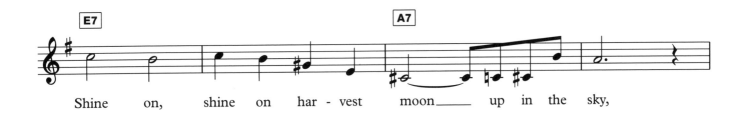

Shine on, shine on har - vest moon_____ up in the sky,

I ain't had no lov - in' since Jan-u-a-ry, Feb-ru-a-ry,

June or Ju - ly._____ Snow time ain't no time to

stay_____ out - doors and spoon, so shine on,

shine on har - vest moon, for me and my gal._____

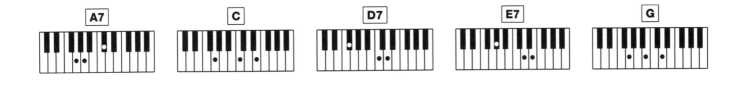

# Strollin'

Words and Music by Ralph Reader

**Suggested Registration:** Accordian
**Rhythm:** Swing
**Tempo:** ♩ = 152

Stroll - in',_____

_____ just stroll - in',_____ in the cool of the

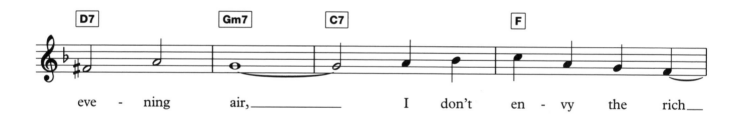

eve - ning air,_____ I don't en - vy the rich__

_____ in their au - to - mo - biles,_____ for a

mo - tor car is pho - ney, I'd ra - ther have shank - s's

# There Is A Tavern In The Town

Traditional

**Suggested Registration:** Clarinet
**Rhythm:** March
**Tempo:** ♩ = 104

There is a tav - ern in the town, in the town, and

there my dear love sits him down, sits him down, and__ drinks his wine 'mid the

laugh - ter__ free, and ne - ver, ne - ver thinks of me. Fare thee

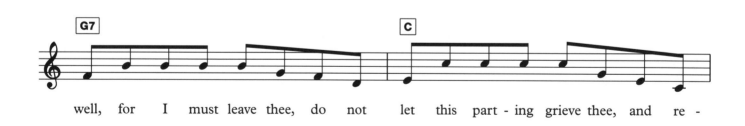

well, for I must leave thee, do not let this part - ing grieve thee, and re -

- mem - ber that the best of friends must part, must part. A - dieu, a - dieu, kind friends, a -

-dieu, a-dieu, a-dieu, I can no long-er stay with you, stay with you,__ I'll__

hang my harp on a weep-ing wil-low tree, and may the world go well with

thee. Fare thee well, for I must leave thee, do not let this part-ing grieve thee, and re-

-mem-ber that the best of friends must part, must part. A-dieu, a-dieu, kind friends, a-

-dieu, a-dieu, a-dieu, I can no long-er stay with you, stay with you,__ I'll__

hang my harp on a weep-ing wil-low tree, and may the world go well with thee.

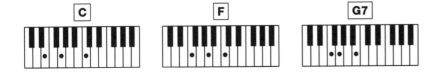

# Toot Toot Tootsie, Goo'bye

Words and Music by Gus Kahn, Ernest Erdman and Dan Russo

**Suggested Registration:** Vibraphone
**Rhythm:** Swing
**Tempo:** ♩ = 200

Toot toot, Toot - sie, goo' - bye,_____

toot toot, Toot - sie, don't cry._____

The choo - choo train that takes me,

a - way from you, no words can tell how

sad it makes me. Kiss me Toot - sie and

then,_____ do it o - ver a -

# We'll Keep A Welcome

Words by Lyn Joshua and James Harper / Music by Mai Jones

**Suggested Registration:** Strings
**Rhythm:** Soft Rock
**Tempo:** ♩ = 84

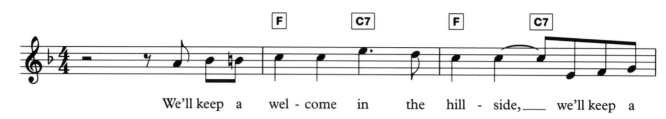

We'll keep a wel-come in the hill-side,___ we'll keep a

wel-come in the glen,___ this land you know will still be

sing-ing,___ when you come home sweet home a-gain.___ There'll be a

friend-ly light to guide you,___ for your re-turn we'll al-ways

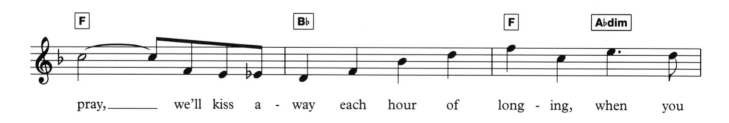

pray,___ we'll kiss a-way each hour of long-ing, when you

come home a-gain some day.___ We'll keep a wel-come in the

# WHEN FATHER PAPERED THE PARLOUR

Words and Music by R P Weston and Fred Barnes

**Suggested Registration:** Clarinet
**Rhythm:** 6/8 March
**Tempo:** ♩. = 96

When Fa - ther pa - pered the par - lour, you

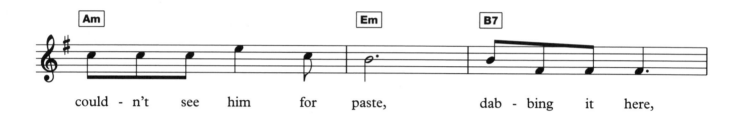

could - n't see him for paste, dab - bing it here,

dab - bing it there, paste and pa - per ev - ery - where.

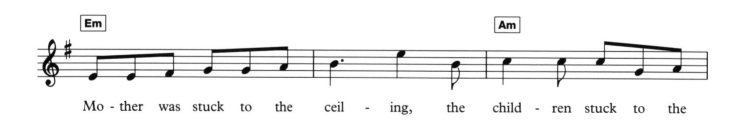

Mo - ther was stuck to the ceil - ing, the child - ren stuck to the

floor,_____ I ne - ver knew a bloom - ing fa - mi - ly

# When I'm Cleaning Windows

Words by Harry Gifford and Fred Cliffe / Music by George Formby

**Suggested Registration:** Honky Tonk Piano
**Rhythm:** Dixie
**Tempo:** ♩ = 200

It's a job that just suits me, a win-dow clean-er

you would be, if you could see what I can see,

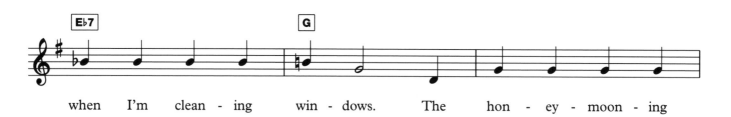

when I'm clean-ing win-dows. The hon-ey-moon-ing

cou-ples too, you should see them bill and coo, you'd

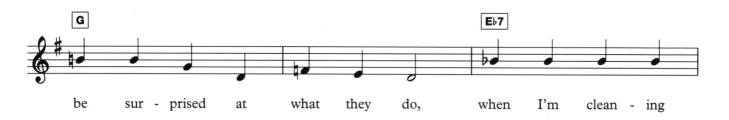

be sur-prised at what they do, when I'm clean-ing

win-dows. In my pro-fes-sion I work hard,

but I'll ne - ver stop, I'll climb this blink - ing

lad - der, till I get right to the top. The

blush - ing bride, she looks di - vine, the bride - groom, he is

do - ing fine. I'd ra - ther have his job than mine,

when I'm clean - ing win - dows.

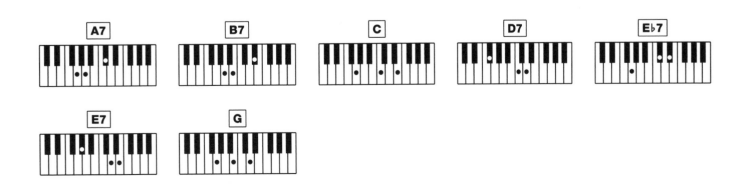

# When You Were Sweet Sixteen

Words and Music by James Thornton

**Suggested Registration:** Acoustic Guitar
**Rhythm:** Swing
**Tempo:** ♩ = 132

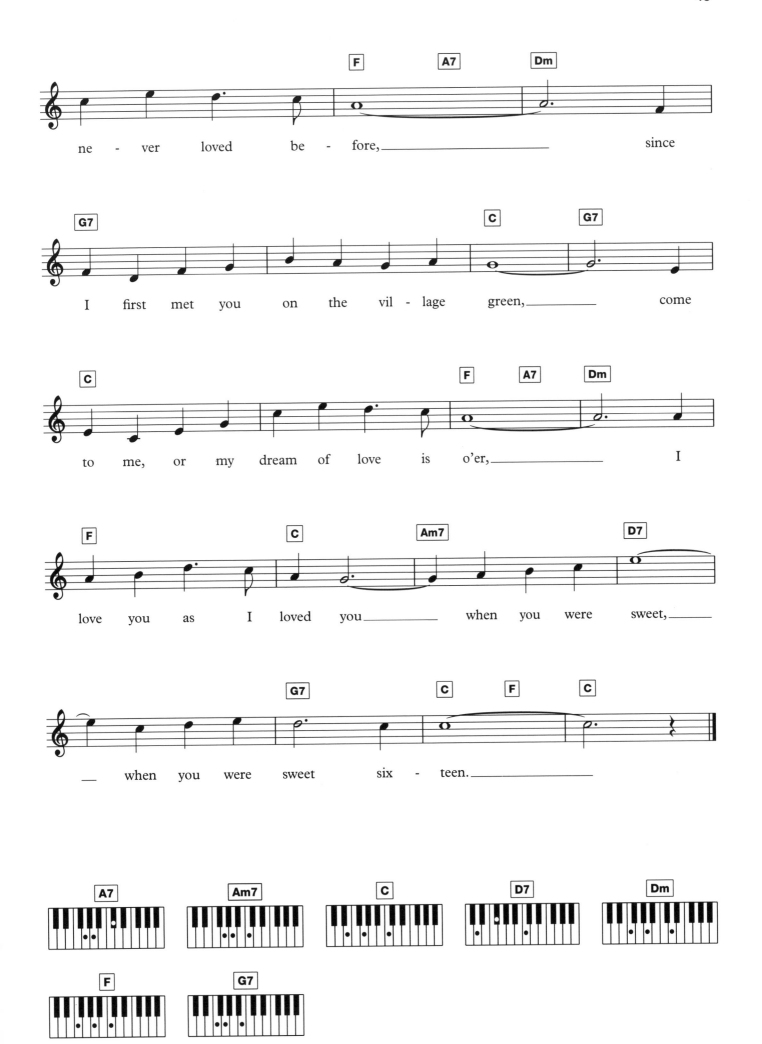

# Who's Taking You Home Tonight

Words and Music by Tommie Connor and Manning Sherwin

**Suggested Registration:** Strings
**Rhythm:** Waltz
**Tempo:** ♩ = 126

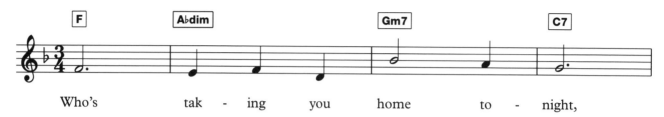

Who's tak - ing you home to - night,

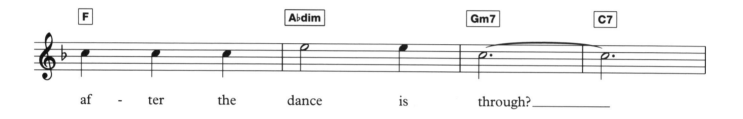

af - ter the dance is through? _____

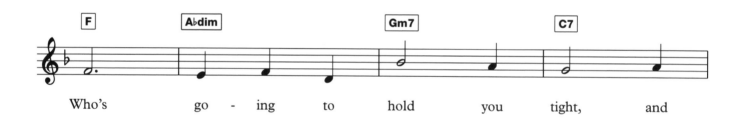

Who's go - ing to hold you tight, and

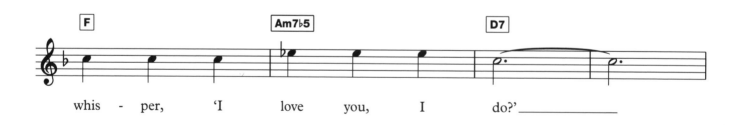

whis - per, 'I love you, I do?' _____

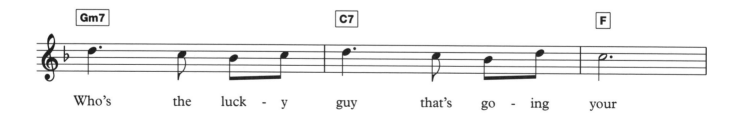

Who's the luck - y guy that's go - ing your

## The Easy Keyboard Library

# An expansive series of over 50 titles!

Each song features melody line, vocals, chord displays, suggested registrations and rhythm settings.

"For each title ALL the chords (both 3 finger and 4 finger) used
are shown in the correct position – which makes a change!"
*Organ & Keyboard Cavalcade*

Each song appears on two facing pages,
eliminating the need to turn the page during performance.

| | | | |
|---|---|---|---|
| The 00s | The Essential Chord Dictionary | Latin Collection | Shirley Bassey |
| Big Band Hits | Favourite Hymns | Love Songs Vol 1 | Showtunes Vol 1 |
| Billy Joel | The Fifties | Love Songs Vol 2 | The Sixties |
| Blues | Film Classics | Motown Classics | Soft Rock Collection |
| Broadway | The Forties | Music Hall | Soul Classics |
| Celebration Songs | Frank Sinatra | Nat King Cole | The Thirties |
| Christmas Carols | George & Ira Gershwin | The Nineties | Traditional Irish Favourites |
| Christmas Songs | George Michael | No.1 Hits Vol 1 | TV Themes |
| Classic Hits Vol 1 | Gilbert & Sullivan | No.1 Hits Vol 2 | The Twenties |
| Classic Hits Vol 2 | Glenn Miller | Popular Classics | Wartime Collection |
| Cliff Richard | Great Songwriters | Pub Singalong Collection | West End Hits |
| Cole Porter | I Try & 10 More Chart Hits | Queen | Whitney Houston |
| Country Songs | Instrumental Classics | Rock 'n' Roll Classics | |
| Disco | James Bond | Scott Joplin | |
| The Eighties | Jazz Classics | The Seventies | |

To buy Faber Music publications or to find out about the full range of titles available
please contact your local music retailer or Faber Music sales enquiries:

Faber Music Ltd, Burnt Mill, Elizabeth Way, Harlow CM20 2HX
Tel: +44 (0) 1279 82 89 82   Fax: +44 (0) 1279 82 89 83
sales@fabermusic.com   fabermusic.com   expressprintmusic.com